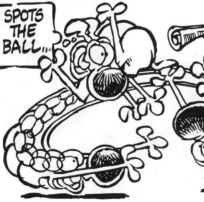

BYE, KIDS, I'LL BE BACK LATER.

QUICK, SHE'S GONE...NOW'S OUR CHANCE, ATTILA... THE VACUUM CLEANER IS ASLEEP!

THE ONLY TIME YOU CAN DESTROY A VACUUM IS WHEN IT'S LYING DORMANT.

10 30

TELL ME, WHY DO WE WANT TO DESTROY THE VACUUM?

IF YOU LEAVE THEM ALONE THEY START TO MULTIPLY.

HEY, WHAT LUCK.. HERE'S A ROPE ATTACHED TO THE VACUUM, YOU TIE HIM UP...

AND I'LL STICK THE OTHER END TO THE WALL SO IT CAN'T RUN AWAY.

10-31

ZIT

BRRRRRRRRRR

SMART MOVE, DR. FRANKENSTEIN.

DUM DUM, DUM DUM, DUM DUM...

11-1

DID YOU HEAR SOMETHING?

ME NEITHER.

NO.

BRRRAA AAAAA AAAAPP

IT'S SHAMU THE KILLER VACUUM...!

MOTHER GOOSE and GRIMM'S NIGHT OF THE LIVING VACUUM!

by Mike Peters

A TRUMPET CLUB SPECIAL EDITION

Published by The Trumpet Club
1540 Broadway, New York, New York 10036

ISBN 0-440-84035-X

This edition published by arrangement with
Pharos Books

Printed in the United States of America
November 1992

10 9 8 7 6 5 4 3 2
CWO

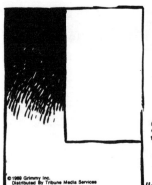

Panel 1: WELL, ATTILA, WE'VE HIT JUST ABOUT EVERY-THING SO FAR...

Panel 2: ELECTRIC WIRES, TV CABLE, WATER PIPES... I GUESS THERE'S NOTHING DOWN THERE LEFT TO HIT...

Panel 3: SNIFF... SNIFF...

Panel 4: DO YOU SMELL GAS?

Panel 5: WELL IT WASN'T ME.

Panel 6: WHY DID YOU HAPPEN TO CHOOSE THIS SPOT TO DIG IN?

Panel 7: BECAUSE THE GROUND IS A LOT SOFTER HERE.

Panel 8: BUT YOU'RE DESTROYING THE GOOSES FLOWER BED.

Panel 9: I NEVER PROMISED HER A ROSE GARDEN.

Panel 10: SEE, ATTILA... THE SECRET TO DIGGING A GREAT HOLE IS...

Panel 11: SET YOUR SIGHTS LOW AND YOU'LL ALWAYS SUCCEED.

Panel 12: BLIP.

Panel 13: WORDS TO LIVE BY...

Mother Goose & GRIMM

BY MIKE PETERS

I LOVE THE NEW YEAR, ATTILA, IT'S A CHANCE TO CHANGE BAD HABITS AND TO START OFF WITH A CLEAN SLATE.

TAKE THIS TRASH CAN FOR INSTANCE...IN THE PAST I COULDN'T WALK BY A TRASH CAN WITHOUT WANTING TO KNOW WHAT WAS IN IT....

I'D HAVE TO PUSH IT OVER, AND MAKE A REAL, LOUD CRASH ,,THEN I'D START TO RUMMAGE THROUGH THE LITTER....

TRASH AND PAPER WOULD BLOW ALL OVER THE STREET..

PEOPLE WOULD BE YELLING AND THROWING THINGS WHILE I'D BE CHEWING ON SOME DISGUSTING PIECE OF GARBAGE...IT WAS AWFUL, JUST AWFUL.

CRASH

...A DOG'S GOTTA DO WHAT A DOG'S GOTTA DO.

OH NO,, SHE'S TAKING US TO THE VET, WE'RE DEAD MEAT!

ALL THE DOORS AND WINDOWS ARE LOCKED, WE'RE TRAPPED ... TRAPPED LIKE RATS!!

THE ONLY THING THAT CAN SAVE US NOW IS PRAYER...

SAY, WHO DO DOGS PRAY TO?

ST. BERNARD,

I BROUGHT IN MY DOG FOR AN APPOINTMENT WITH THE VET...

YES, MA'AM, THE DOCTOR IS GETTING THE TRANQUILIZER DART READY.

OH, I DON'T REALLY THINK GRIMMY WILL NEED THAT...

WE KNOW... IT'S FOR THE DOCTOR.

3-31

GRIMMY ALWAYS GETS A LITTLE NERVOUS WHEN HE COMES TO THE VET...

YES, MA'AM, NOW WHAT SEEMS TO BE YOUR DOG'S PROBLEM?

WELL, FIRST IF YOU COULD PRY HIM OFF THE ELEVATOR MAN.

THIS IS AWFUL, WE'RE TRAPPED HERE IN THE VET'S OFFICE 18 FLOORS UP.

WILL YOU RELAX, HE'S A VET, HE'S HERE TO HELP US.

...IF THERE'S ANYTHING WRONG WITH US, THE VET WILL HAVE US FIXED.

HEY, WHO OPENED THIS WINDOW?

4/10

FIXED, ATTILA, THEY'RE GOING TO HAVE US FIXED!

I KNOW IT... DOGS CAN SENSE THESE THINGS... THAT'S WHY SHE BROUGHT US HERE TO THE VET..

I DON'T WANT TO BE FIXED...

...I WANT TO STAY BROKEN.

4-11

THIS IS AWFUL... HERE I AM...COLD, FRIGHTENED, HYSTERICAL...

AT THE END OF MY WITS, TOTALLY STRUNG OUT, STANDING ON THE LEDGE OF A BUILDING...

...AND NOW SOME DOCTOR IS GOING TO HAVE ME NEUTERED...

I THINK I SAW THIS ONCE ON GERALDO.

4/12

IT'S UNBELIEVABLE, I'M THIRTY YEARS OLD, BUT I DON'T LOOK IT.

I STILL HAVE THAT SAME YOUNG, ADORABLE FACE AS I DID WHEN I WAS FOUR...

© 1989 Grimmy Inc.
Distributed By Tribune Media Services

I WONDER IF DICK CLARK DOES THIS EVERY NIGHT.?

5-4

I CAN'T BE THIRTY, I'M ONLY FOUR...I'M STILL A PUPPY...

LOOK, PUPPIES LIKE PLAYING WITH YARN, SEE I'M A PUPPY, GOO, GOO, GAA...

GOO GOO...DA DA, GAA GAA, GOO GOO, DAA DAA, GAA...ER.. OOPS,...

© 1989 Grimmy Inc.
Distributed By Tribune Media Services

...I'M NOT GETTING OLDER, I'M GETTING SENILE.

5-5

© 1989 Grimmy Inc.
Distributed By Tribune Media Services

5-6

ZOOM

BONK

GRIMM, WHAT ARE YOU DOING?

...IT'S BETTER TO BURN OUT THAN TO RUST OUT.

Panel 1: IS GRIMMY GETTING OVER THE FACT THAT HE'S THIRTY?

Panel 2: OH, YEAH... HE SPENT ALL YESTERDAY LOOKING FOR WRINKLES AND AGE SPOTS, BUT I'M SURE HE'S GOTTEN OVER IT...

Panel 3: I THINK THIS DOG WANTS SOME RETIN-A.

Panel 4: GRIMMY... LOOK AT THIS MESS ALL OVER THE SOFA!

Panel 5: THIS HAPPENS EVERY SPRING... I HATE WHEN YOU START SHEDDING.

Panel 6: WHEN YOU'RE THIRTY, IT'S NOT CALLED SHEDDING...

Panel 7: ...IT'S CALLED MALE PATTERNED BALDNESS.

5-9

Panel 8: I BLEW IT... I LOST MY CHILDHOOD. ALL THOSE PRECIOUS MOMENTS...

Panel 9: I WENT THROUGH THE BEST YEARS OF MY LIFE WITHOUT EVEN KNOWING IT.

Panel 10: REMEMBER, ATTILA, IN LIFE, YOU ONLY GO AROUND...

Panel 11: ...NINE TIMES.

Panel 12: I HATE CATS.

5/10

I'M THIRTY YEARS OLD, AND LOOK AT ALL THE THINGS I'VE MISSED... I'VE NEVER PLAYED BASEBALL...

I'VE NEVER DOUBLE DATED... I'VE NEVER GIVEN ANYONE A HICKEY...

5-11

DON'T EVEN THINK ABOUT IT.

ATTILA, I'M GOING TO RECAPTURE MY YOUTH AND MAKE UP FOR LOST TIME...

AND EXPERIENCE EVERYTHING I'VE MISSED IN MY CHILDHOOD...

AND JUST HOW ARE WE GOING TO DO THAT, RIN TIN TIN?

5/12

RALPH, THERE'S A DOG OUTSIDE THROWING ROLLS OF TOILET PAPER IN OUR ELM TREE.

I CAN'T BELIEVE IT, I'M THIRTY IN DOG YEARS, MY BODY IS FALLING APART.

...EVERY SECOND I'M GETTING OLDER AND OLDER,

5-13

TICK TOCK, TICK TOCK, TICK TOCK, TICK TOCK...

TICK, TOCK, TICK,

PLEASE, NOT DURING PEE WEE HERMAN.

Panel 1: LOOK, GRIMMY, IT'S ONE OF YOUR SISTER'S PUPPIES...HIS NAME IS REX.

Panel 2: ISN'T HE ADORABLE? WE'RE GOING TO BABY-SIT HIM FOR A WHILE. I LOVE HOW HE GOES "YIP."

YIP YIP YIP YIP

5-15

Panel 3: YIP YIP YIP YIP YIP YIP YIP YIP YIP

Panel 4: I GUESS "YIP" IS PUPPY FOR "COO!"

YIP YIP YIP

Panel 5: OH NO...THAT LITTLE PUPPY IS MAKING MESSES ALL OVER THE FLOOR...

Panel 6: THERE ARE STAINS AND SPOTS EVERYWHERE...HE'S TURNED THIS PLACE INTO A DISASTER AREA...

5/16

Panel 7: WE'VE GOT TO STOP...AH, ER...SAY, WHAT IS HIS NAME AGAIN?

Panel 8: REX...BUT I CALL HIM REXXON.

YIP YIP YIP YIP

Panel 9: NO, NO, REXXON, WIDOW PUPPY-KINS JUST MADE ANOTHER MESSY. MUMMY DOESN'T WIKE MESSIES...

Panel 10: MUMMY IS TWY-ING TO KEEP THE HOUSE QWEEN...UNDER-STAND, BOO-BOO-KINS?

Panel 11: YUCK...HE DID IT AGAIN!

3/17

Panel 12: SOMETIMES, WIDOW REXXON JUST CAN'T HELP IT.

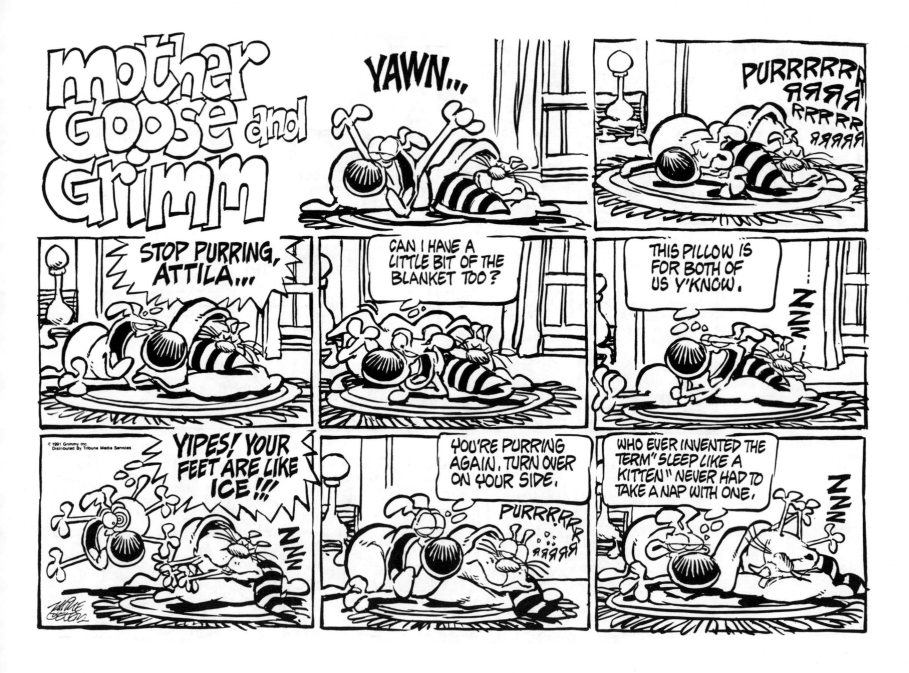

ONE WRONG MOVE WITH THIS STUFF AND YOU'RE HISTORY,

8-5

© 1988 Tribune Media Services, Inc.
All Rights Reserved

SOMETIMES I DO THINGS I FEEL SO ASHAMED OF...

FORTUNATELY, IT USUALLY DOESN'T LAST VERY LONG,

© 1988 Tribune Media Services, Inc.
All Rights Reserved

NO, NO, WIDOW BOO BOO, THESE ARE MY POTTED PLANTS, THEY ARE WEO-WEE, WEO-WEE SPECIAL...

MUMMY DOESN'T WANT WIDOW PUPPY TO USE HER FLOWERS AS HIS LITTER-BOX...OK? NOW, GO OUT AND PWAY,

GOOD LORD, HE'S DOING IT AGAIN...

♪WHOOPS..THERE GOES ANOTHER RUBBER TREE PLANT..♪

5-25

© 1989 Grimmy Inc.
Distributed By Tribune Media Services

OH, GRIMMY..I THINK LITTLE REXXON HAS FINALLY LEARNED WHAT THE YARD IS FOR....

YIP YIP YIP!

..YEAH, HIDING,

WHOOSH

5-26   © 1989 Grimmy Inc.
Distributed By Tribune Media Services

YES, YES...I'D LOVE TO SEE A FREE DEMONSTRATION.

BRUSHES

© 1989 Grimmy Inc.
Distributed By Tribune Media Services

5-27

MOTHER GOOSE AND GRIMM BY MIKE PETERS

HEY, LOOK AT THIS! THEY SAY NO TWO SNOW FLAKES LOOK ALIKE.

BUT THESE TWO FLAKES LOOK EXACTLY THE SAME.

I DID IT... I FOUND TWO IDENTICAL SNOW FLAKES.

I DID IT... OF ALL THE BILLIONS OF SNOW FLAKES, I FOUND THE TWO THAT MATCH. THEY'LL PUT ME IN THE GUINESS BOOK OF RECORDS.

© 1991 Grimmy, Inc.
Distributed By Tribune Media Services

I FOUND THE FLAKE! I FOUND THE FLAKE!

I THINK I'M TALKING TO THE FLAKE.

Mother Goose & Grimm

OHMYGOSH... IT'S THE GIRL OF MY DREAMS, THAT CUTE LITTLE FRENCH POODLE. ALL BY HERSELF ON A SUMMER EVENING.

I'VE BEEN WAITING TO BE ALONE WITH HER FOR MONTHS. GO ON, GRIMMY, NOW'S YOUR CHANCE TO TELL HER HOW YOU FEEL.

TELL HER THAT SHE WALKS IN BEAUTY LIKE THE NIGHT, OF CLOUDLESS CLIMES AND STARRY SKIES...

...AND ALL THAT'S BEST OF DARK AND BRIGHT, MEET IN HER ASPECT AND HER EYES.

GO ON... TELL HER...

ARF

...THIS IS SO DEPRESSING.

6-10

Mother Goose & GRIMM

BY MIKE PETERS

Panel 1: MZ GOOSE....I'M CONFUSED, CAN YOU TELL ME THE DIFFERENCE BETWEEN MICHELANGELO AND LEONARDO?

Panel 2: WHY YES, HAM, I'M JUST AMAZED THAT YOU'RE INTERESTED IN ART.

Panel 3: LET'S SEE....LEONARDO AND MICHELANGELO WERE CONTEMPORARIES...

Panel 4: LEONARDO WAS A GREAT PAINTER...HIS MOST FAMOUS PAINTINGS WERE THE MONA LISA AND THE LAST SUPPER.

Panel 5: MICHELANGELO WAS A GREAT PAINTER AND SCULPTOR, HIS STATUES CONVEYED A SENSE OF GRANDEUR....AND POWER.

Panel 6: HIS MOST FAMOUS PAINTINGS WERE THE FRESCOES ON THE CEILING OF THE SISTINE CHAPEL, NOW THEN...DOES THAT HELP?

Panel 7: WELL, NOT REALLY... PSST...

Panel 8: LEONARDO HAS A BLUE MASK, MICHELANGELO HAS ORANGE.

OH, BOY... THIS SAYS THERE'S A SPECIAL DOGGIE *TOY* WITH EVERY BOX OF FIDO FOOGIES...

...AND IT'S GUARANTEED TO KEEP A DOG ENTERTAINED FOR HOURS.

OKAY, WHERE IS IT?

IT'S GOT TO BE IN HERE SOMEWHERE.

I LOVE DOGGIE TOYS.

I MUST BE GETTING CLOSER...

...I'M ALMOST AT THE BOTTOM.

WAIT... I THINK I'VE FOUND IT.

I DID, I DID, I FINALLY FOUND THE DOGGIE TOY...

...IT'S THE BOX.

Mother Goose & Grimm

BY MIKE PETERS

ALL RIGHT, COME ON GRIMMY.

OH BOY... DOGS LOVE RIDING IN CARS.

WE LOVE RACING DOWN THE STREETS.

WE LOVE SITTING WITH OUR HEADS OUT THE WINDOWS.

WE LOVE THE SUDDEN TURNS AND THE SCREECHING STOPS,

WE LOVE THE HILLS, THE CURVES, THE BUMPS, THE FLASHING LIGHTS...

...THE BEEPING HORNS, THE SCREAMING SIRENS, DOGS LOVE EVERY-THING ABOUT CARS...

...CATS, ON THE OTHER HAND...

Mother Goose & GRIMM

I'M STARVING. LET'S HAVE SOME BRUNCH.

I LOVE BRUNCH. SEE BRUNCH IS BETWEEN BREAKFAST AND LUNCH.

...THAT MEANS THAT LUPPER IS BETWEEN LUNCH AND SUPPER.

THEN SPAWN IS BETWEEN SUPPER AND DAWN...

AND SCRUNCH IS BETWEEN SCRAPS AND BRUNCH...

SNALPO IS BETWEEN SNACKS AND ALPO...

GOLIVES IS BETWEEN GARBAGE AND OLIVES...

YICKLES IS BETWEEN YOGURT AND PICKLES...

HELLO IS BETWEEN HAIR BALLS AND JELLO...

FUNNY, I'M NOT HUNGRY ANY MORE...

I THINK I'M GOING TO SPIT UP...

© 1990 Grimmy Inc.
Distributed By Tribune Media Services

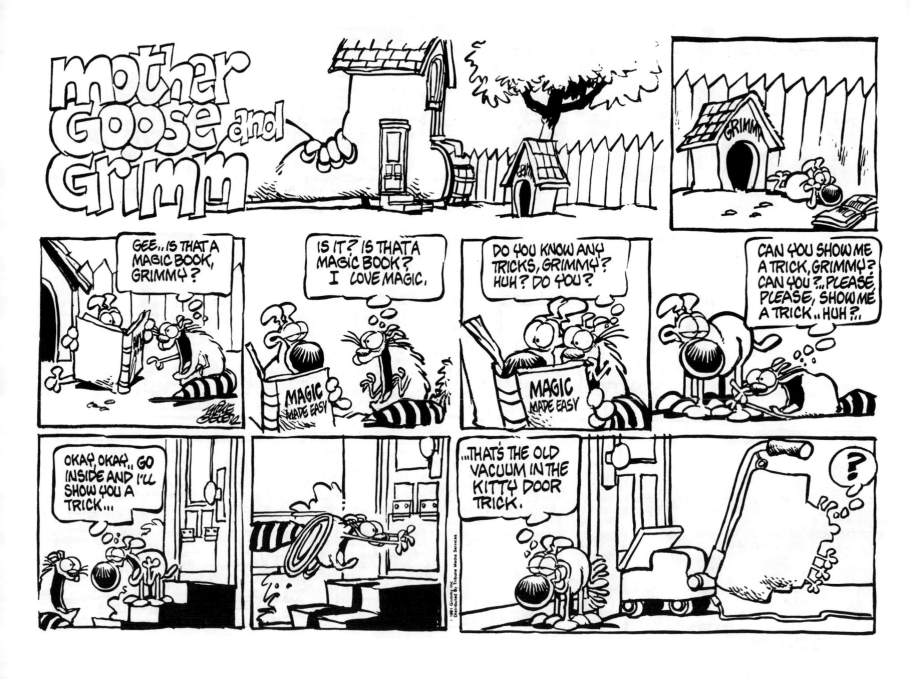

GEE, THIS DOG FOOD MAKES ITS OWN GRAVY WHEN YOU ADD WATER.

WHAT A CONVENIENT AND TIME-SAVING HELP FOR ANY HOMEMAKER ....

DOMESTICATED, I'M BECOMING DOMESTICATED.

GOSH, MY DOGGY DISH IS SO SPARKLING CLEAN, I CAN ALMOST SEE MY FACE IN IT ....

..WHEN YOU'RE DOMESTICATED, LITTLE THINGS TURN YOU ON.

GRIMMY, WHAT'S WRONG WITH YOU ? ....

ARE YOU SICK? ARE YOU HUNGRY?

I'M DOMESTICATED.

YOU'RE WEIRD.

I CAN'T BELIEVE IT, SHE'S BRAINWASHED ME...

I'VE BECOME DOMESTICATED, I HAVE NO WILL OF MY OWN.

I DO TRICKS ON COMMAND, I COME WHEN CALLED... I'M A ZOMBIE...

...I'M THE DOG OF THE LIVING DEAD.

7-6

I'M NOT DOMESTICATED, I'M STILL THE WILD, SAVAGE, PRIMITIVE BEAST...

WHO COULD ESCAPE INTO THE WILDERNESS ANYTIME I WANTED TO...

...JUST BY BITING DOWN ON THIS LEASH WITH MY FEROCIOUS TEETH...

...BUT I DON'T WANT TO BREAK MY CAPS.

7-7

I'LL PROVE I'M NOT DOMESTICATED, I'M GOING TO START LIVING ON THE EDGE.

7-8

JUST ME AGAINST NATURE, ROUGHING IT, BRAVING THE ELEMENTS...

THERE... I'VE UNPLUGGED MY ELECTRIC BLANKET.

IT MUST BE FUN TO BE A BIG STAR LIKE CARL THE WONDER POODLE....

YOU CAN TELL HE HAS BECOME A REALLY BIG STAR...

....HE GOT AN UNLISTED DOG TAG.

CARL THE WONDER POODLE IS MY HERO.

I WANT TO BE JUST LIKE HIM...

....EXCEPT FOR THE WAY HE STAINS THE RUG WHENEVER HE GETS EXCITED.

OH, BOY... TODAY CARL THE WONDER POODLE IS PLAYING A FAMOUS HOLLYWOOD TV DOG....

BUT ALL OF THE DOGS WRITERS HAVE GONE ON STRIKE BECAUSE OF BAD WORKING CONDITIONS...

SO, FOR THE LAST HALF HOUR, CARL HAS JUST STOOD THERE WAGGING HIS TAIL ...

....HOW DO THEY KEEP COMING UP WITH THESE GREAT PLOTS?

Mother Goose and Grimm
BY Mike Peters

THERE'S TWELVE PIECES OF GUM UNDER THIS TABLE...

THE BASEBOARD NEEDS DUSTING...

© 1990 Grimmy Inc
Distributed By Tribune Media Services

NICE CUFFS...

GEE,, THERE'S TWO PAPER CLIPS AND A FUZZ BALL...

GROSS, LOOK AT THE MESS UNDER THIS SINK...

...IT'S AMAZING WHAT YOU NOTICE WHEN YOU'RE ONE FOOT TALL.

HOW, ATTILA... HOW COULD THIS HAPPEN TO ME?

ONE MINUTE I'M JUST AN AVERAGE, NORMAL, HAPPY-GO-LUCKY DOG...

..THE NEXT MINUTE I'M A LOW-INCOME HOUSING PROJECT! HOW? HOW?

MAYBE YOUR FLEAS KNOW SOMEONE AT HUD.

8-24

I CAN'T UNDERSTAND WHY PEOPLE DON'T LIKE FLEAS? THEY MAKE GREAT PETS.

THEY'RE QUIET, FAITHFUL, EASY TO TAKE CARE OF, THEY'D FOLLOW YOU ANYWHERE ...

YOU CAN OWN AS MANY AS YOU WANT AND THEY DON'T COST YOU ANY MONEY ...

..THE BEST THINGS IN LIFE ARE FLEAS.

8-25

YUCK.... GET OUT OF HERE, FLIES.

GRIM

8/26

I DON'T BELIEVE THIS.. SHE'S TYING ME UP TO A TREE.. NO TRIAL... NO JURY... SHE DIDN'T EVEN READ ME MY RIGHTS....

AREN'T I ALLOWED TO HAVE A LAWYER? IS THIS FAIR? IS THIS CONSTITUTIONAL?

DOES TED KOPPEL KNOW ABOUT THIS ?!!

9-11

DON'T LOOK AT ME LIKE THAT, GRIMMY.. I'VE GOT TO TIE YOU UP BECAUSE YOU ALWAYS RUN AWAY...

NO, I WON'T.. I PROMISE.. I'VE GROWN OUT OF THAT.. I LOVE IT HERE.. REALLY.. I WON'T RUN AWAY.. TRUST ME.. RELATIONSHIP IS BASED ON TRUST....

OKAY, OKAY, I TRUST YOU.. STAY THERE AND I'LL BRING OUT YOUR WATER.

ZING...

9-12

WHAT'S WRONG? YOU LOOK UPSET.

OH, GRIMMY GOT OUT THIS MORNING AND I THINK HE MIGHT BE LOST.

DON'T WORRY, MOST DOGS STAY WITHIN A ONE BLOCK AREA OF THEIR HOME.... HE WON'T GO FAR.

CHINA.

AIR

9-13

Mother Goose and Grimm BY MIKE PETERS

MUNCH MUNCH MUNCH

ATTIL

I HATE CATS...THEY DON'T HAVE TO DO ANYTHING. THEY JUST SLEEP AND EAT.

ATTILA

BUT DOGS HAVE TO DO EVERYTHING!! WE HAVE TO FETCH AND HEAL AND CATCH FRISBEES...

ATTIL

...WE HAVE TO GUARD THE HOUSE AND BRING PEOPLE THEIR SLIPPERS AND GO FOR WALKS ON A LEASH...

WE HAVE TO SIT OR STAY OR ROLL-OVER OR SPEAK OR BEG OR SHAKE HANDS OR DO ANY OF THE STUPID TRICKS PEOPLE MAKE US DO...

BUT CATS DON'T HAVE TO DO ANYTHING USEFUL, DO THEY? HUH?!! HUH? TELL ME ONE USEFUL THING THAT A CAT DOES?!!

.....WE INTIMIDATE DOGS.

BOY, OH, BOY... THIS IS REALLY FUN, LIVING IN THE FOREST.

I CAN GO ANYWHERE I WANT TO GO, DO ANYTHING I WANT TO DO...

AND EAT FROM THE FOUR BASIC FOOD GROUPS...

"FLYING, CRAWLING, SLITHERING AND HOPPING.

IF I DON'T EAT SOMETHING SOON I'LL STARVE, BUT THE ONLY THING I CAN CATCH ARE WORMS.

FAT, SLIMY, DISGUSTING WORMS... HOW CAN BIRDS SWALLOW THESE THINGS WITHOUT GAGGING?

SAY... DO YOU HAVE ANY GREY POUPON?

I'M NOT AFRAID OF BEING OUT HERE AT NIGHT.

SLEEPING IN THE WOODS IS JUST LIKE SLEEPING AT HOME...

"EXCEPT WITH YOUR EYES OPEN.

Panel 1: WHY AM I HAVING SUCH A HARD TIME FINDING SOMETHING TO EAT?

Panel 2: LOTS OF ANIMALS SURVIVE IN THE WOODS. THERE'S MORE THAN ENOUGH FOOD.

Panel 3: YOU'VE JUST GOT TO KNOW WHERE TO LOOK.

Panel 4: LET'S SEE... WHERE'S THE TREE THAT GROWS RICE CRISPY SQUARES?

Panel 1: LOBO, THE JUNGLE WOLF, HID IN THE BUSHES FOR HIS UNSUSPECTING PREY. SUDDENLY HIS HAWK-LIKE EYES SPOTTED A FIELD MOUSE.

Panel 2: INSTANTLY, WITH MUSCLES LIKE TEMPERED STEEL, HE POUNCED UPON HIS VICTIM.... BONK!

Panel 4: BUT THEN LOBO GAVE HIM C.P.R. AND PROMISED TO TAKE HIM TO THE CIRCUS IF HE GOT BETTER.

Panel 1: HELLO....I'M BACK! IT'S GREAT TO BE BACK HOME.

Panel 2: GEE, I DIDN'T REALIZE HOW MUCH I'VE MISSED EVERYTHING.... HELLO, DOOR KNOB....

Panel 3: HELLO, FLOWER POT... HELLO, LAMP SHADE....

Panel 4: HELLO, POND SCUM.

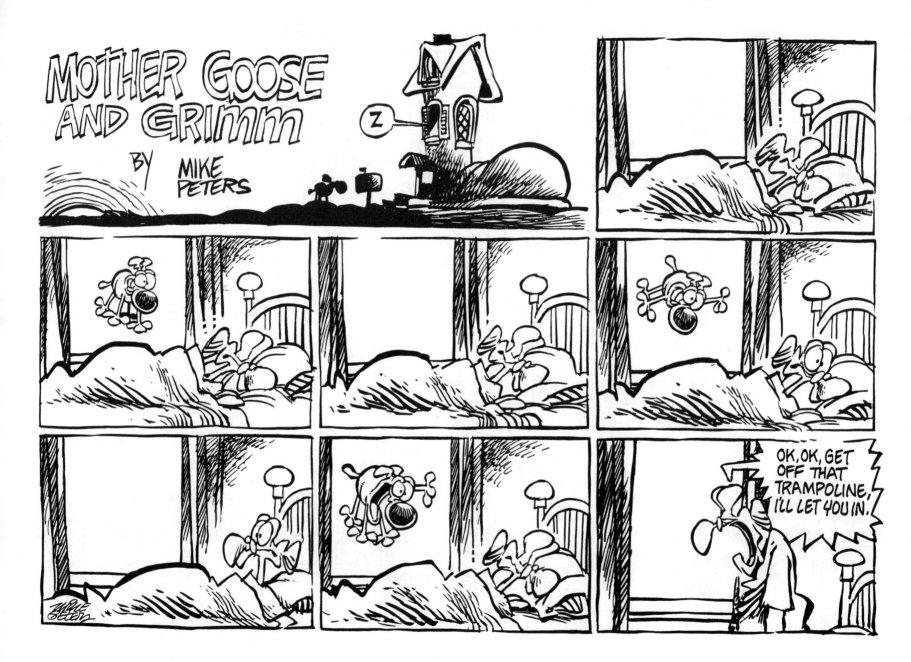

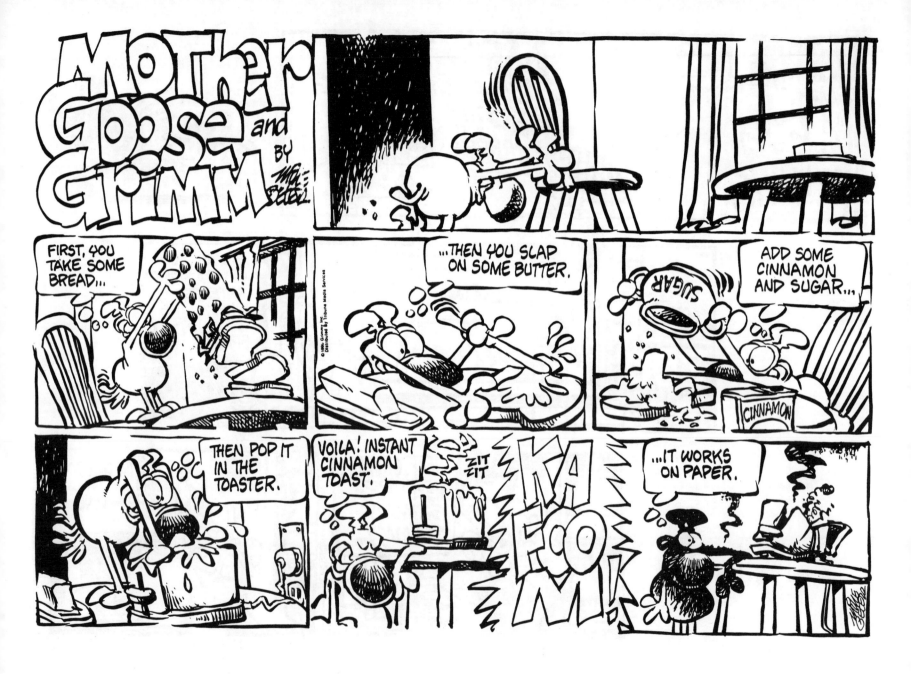

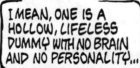

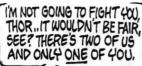

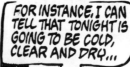

BRRR....

SEE, WHEN IT'S REALLY COLD OUT, ALL YOU HAVE TO DO IS FIND A STREET GRATE.

THE GOVERNMENT MAKES SURE THAT EVERY HOMELESS PERSON HAS ONE STREET GRATE TO SLEEP ON...

THEN THEY WRAP THEMSELVES UP IN A TRASH BAG AND HUDDLE AROUND A GRATE TO KEEP WARM....PRETTY NEAT, HUH?

NEAT.

IS THIS A GRATE COUNTRY OR WHAT?

HAPPINESS IS A WARM STREET GRATE.

RELAX, ATTILA.. WE CAN LIVE ON THE STREET AS WELL AS THE NEXT GUY...

AUGHHHHHHHHHH

AH, LET ME REPHRASE THAT.

ZING

I CAN'T BELIEVE I LET HIM TALK ME INTO LIVING ON THE STREET...I'M COLD, HUNGRY AND MISERABLE.

11-30

AT LEAST I CAN TAKE COMFORT THAT IT CAN'T GET ANY WORSE...

© 1989 Grimmy Inc. Distributed By Tribune Media Services

HEY, LOOK...IT'S SNOWING...

I'M COLD, HUNGRY, DIRTY, GREASY, I HATE LIVING ON THE STREET, I HATE EATING OUT OF TRASH CANS, I'M MISERABLE AND I WANT TO GO HOME...

KIDS?

HUH?

© 1989 Grimmy Inc. Distributed By Tribune Media Services

12-1

AHH...THE POWER OF POSITIVE WHINING.

GEE, IT'S REALLY GOOD TO BE HOME, BUT I CAN'T BELIEVE WE MISSED OUT ON THANKSGIVING.

SAY...WHEN WAS THANKSGIVING?

© 1989 Grimmy Inc. Distributed By Tribune Media Services

12-2

...THE MINUTE WE WALKED THROUGH THE DOOR.

?

WHAT ARE YOU DOING, GRIMMY?

I'VE GOT TO COUNT HOW MANY FLEAS I'VE GOT LIVING ON MY BACK.

SEE, A DOG CAN'T HAVE MORE THAN 150 ON HIM AT ONE TIME.

THERE ARE FIRE CODES, Y'KNOW.

RIGHT.

ATTILA, I DON'T WANT TO BE JUST A BROKEN-DOWN FLEA MOTEL, I WANT TO BE A GREAT FLEA MOTEL.

I WANT TO OPEN A CHAIN OF FLEA MOTELS ACROSS THE COUNTRY...

SO EVERY FLEA AND TICK TRAVELING AROUND AMERICA, WILL HAVE A WARM DOG TO SLEEP ON.

AND WHAT WILL YOU CALL IT?

CLUB MUTT.

OH SURE, ATTILA, GO ON AND SIT THERE WHILE I DO ALL THE WORK.

RUNNING A FLEA MOTEL IS NOT AS EASY AS IT SOUNDS.

YOU'VE GOT TO THINK OF EVERY LITTLE THING... I MEAN...

HAVE YOU EVER TRIED TO FIND 150 TEENY GIDEON BIBLES?

12-13

Mother Goose & GRIMM

BY MIKE PETERS

I BET IF I RAN REALLY FAST I COULD SNAP THIS THING.

FASTER, FASTER...

IT'S STRETCHING...

IT'S STRETCHING...

© 1990 Grimmy, Inc.
Distributed By Tribune Media Services

BONK...

ZING...

REMIND ME NEVER TO USE A BUNGEE LEASH.

MMMM... WHAT IS IT, GRIMMY?

I JUST OPENED CLUB MUTT, MY NEW FIVE-STAR FLEA MOTEL...

YUCK, GET OFF MY BED...!

YOU'RE COVERED IN FLEAS FROM YOUR HEAD TO YOUR TAIL...

THAT'S NOT MY TAIL...THAT'S THE PRESIDENTIAL SUITE.

WELCOME TO CLUB MUTT, EVERYBODY.

I HOPE YOU INSECTS HAVE A NICE DAY...

AND IF YOU NEED ANYTHING... JUST BUZZ.

SOMETIMES I JUST CRACK ME UP...

HEH HEH HEH HEH

ATTILA...MY FLEA MOTEL IS ALL FILLED UP...

I'VE GOT A CONVENTION OF CARPENTER ANTS COMING TONIGHT AND I NEED HELP.

SO, WHY ARE YOU TELLING ME?

HAVE YOU EVER THOUGHT ABOUT A CAREER IN HOTEL MANAGEMENT?

 I LOVE BEING A FLEA MOTEL ...

 RUMBLERUMBLERUMBLE

 BUT I NEVER SHOULD'VE INSTALLED THOSE VIBRATING BEDS.

 OH OH ... MY FLEA MOTEL IS TOTALLY FULL.

 I CAN'T TAKE ANY MORE BUGS.

 MAYBE I SHOULD TURN ON A "NO VACANCY" SIGN.

 NO...THAT WOULD JUST ATTRACT FLYS.

 ATTILA, I'VE GOT SOMETHING VERY PERSONAL I'VE BEEN CARRYING AROUND, THAT I'D LIKE TO SHARE WITH YOU.

SURE. WHAT IS IT?

 FLEAS!

 MERRY CHRISTMAS.

Panel 1: WAKE UP, ATTILA... WAKE UP, I'VE SEEN IT...THE VACUUM IN THE CLOSET.

Panel 2: LOOK AT THE SIZE OF THAT BAG...DO YOU KNOW WHAT WE'VE FOUND? IT'S...IT'S...

Panel 3: ...THE NEST OF THE QUEEN VACUUM SWEEPER!!!

Panel 4: HERE...YOU'D BETTER WEAR SOME GARLIC AROUND YOUR NECK, I'LL CALL A PRIEST.
HAVE YOU HAD RABIES SHOTS?

Panel 5: IT'S THE NESTING PLACE OF THE QUEEN VACUUM SWEEPER...WE'VE GOT TO DO SOMETHING...

Panel 6: Y'SEE, QUEEN VACUUMS LIE DORMANT IN DARK CLOSETS DURING THE DAY, BUT DURING THE NIGHT THEY ROAM THE HOUSE...

Panel 7: ..DEVOURING EVERYTHING THEY SEE AND LIVING ON THE HAIRBALLS OF INNOCENT DOGS AND CATS.

Panel 8: YOU REALLY GET INTO THIS, DON'T YOU?
SHH...

Panel 9: IF I CAN BITE THROUGH THIS WIRE, THAT VACUUM WILL BE TOAST!

Panel 10: ZIT

Panel 11: WELL, YOU WERE HALF RIGHT.

WAIT A MINUTE...IF THIS IS THE NESTING PLACE OF THE QUEEN VACUUM SWEEPER...

THEN WHY HAVEN'T I SEEN LOTS OF LITTLE VACUUM SWEEPERS RUNNING AROUND?

...THEY EAT THEIR YOUNG.

WE CAN'T GO TO SLEEP, ATTILA, WE'VE GOT TO KEEP OUR EYES ON THIS THING ALL NIGHT.

10-5

WHY?

A WATCHED VACUUM NEVER SUCKS.

OH, NO...I SHORT-CIRCUITED THE VACUUM....RUN, ATTILA, RUN....

10-6

NEVER GET CAUGHT BY THE QUEEN VACUUM SWEEPER...

...YOU'LL HAVE A HICKEY THE SIZE OF A BUICK.

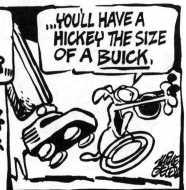

Panel 1: YOU DON'T UNDERSTAND, ATTILA... THE **QUEEN VACUUM** IS ONLY GESTATING RIGHT NOW.

Panel 2: IN A WEEK THERE WILL BE THOUSANDS OF HUNGRY LITTLE VACUUM LARVA ALL OVER THE FLOOR, SPINNING THEIR TINY COCOONS INTO VACUUM BAGS...

Panel 3: ...AND SOON THEY'LL MUTATE INTO LITTLE DUST BUSTERS, AND EVENTUALLY INTO FULL-SIZE VACUUMS...

WHERE DO YOU COME UP WITH THESE THINGS?

Panel 4: I SAW IT ON NATIONAL GEOGRAPHIC.

10-8

Panel: GRIMMY, YOU'VE GOT TO GET OVER THIS FEAR OF VACUUMS, SEE? THEY'RE PERFECTLY HARMLESS.

Panel: I GUESS THESE THINGS TAKE TIME.

10/9

Panel: GRIMMY...WHY ARE WE DOING THIS?

Panel: AS LONG AS THERE'S ONE VACUUM LEFT IN THE WORLD, NO **DOG** WILL BE SAFE.

10-10

Panel: ...HE WENT THAT WAY.